G000017550

Joseph and the Three Gifts

Joseph
and the
Three Gifts

An Angel's Story

BRIAN SIBLEY

Decorations by Henry Martin

DARTON · LONGMAN + TODD

First published in 2019 by
Darton, Longman and Todd Ltd
1 Spencer Court
140–142 Wandsworth High Street
London SW18 4JJ

ISBN 978-0-232-53416-0

A catalogue record for this book is available
from the British Library.

Designed and produced by Judy Linard
Printed and bound in Great Britain by
Bell & Bain, Glasgow

Contents

5

Joseph
and the
Three Gifts

1
Annunciations

So, you want to know about Joseph? And why wouldn't you? Anyone who's heard the story knows the name; he's there in every nativity play and present near the manger in every Christmas crib, while pictures of him and his family drop daily through your letter box every December.

But whilst he's to be found somewhere in thousands of artworks by centuries of painters, he is (as often as not) relegated to the background, shown half in shadow, depicted looking awestruck, or simply puzzled and patient. Or, sometimes, with an expression that is impossible to read: not so much inscrutable as undefined, as though the artist's interests and attentions lay elsewhere, occupied with the far greater burden of depicting the Mother and Child.

Joseph might be shown returning to the stable with a bundle of new-cut firewood or, perhaps, holding up a lantern for the benefit of visiting dignitaries and farm-workers. True he does feature in a couple of ancient carols, but he has never had the prominence of kings, shepherds and, I might add, angels.

Portrayed, more often than not, as an old, white-haired man leaning on a staff; he is the perfect cipher for trust and reliability, a symbolic illustration of faithfulness and stoicism.

That, then, is Joseph: the supporting player in a monumental drama that has been so often

12

told that the enormity of its possibilities has been reduced to the familiar – even to the commonplace.

The Church, of course, made him a Saint – hence those glowing dinner-plate halos which he sports in many representations. There is also, it appears, a field of theological study that goes by the name of Josephology. But, for most people he is simply a character who lives in the margin of the Christmas story.

But, if you want to know about Joseph, I can certainly tell you.

Why me? Well, I'll come to that, soon enough. Having criticised several generations of artists, I should probably start by telling you what he looks like, but then I'm no judge of men's outer appearances – something that will require another explanation anon. But whether Joseph is plain-featured or once-handsome-and-now-rugged is quite unimportant to this story – and to *his* story. What matters is his character, the man within; and about that I can tell you quite enough to provide an adequate introduction. So, that's where we'll start …

Joseph is proud of his heritage, descended, across millennia, from (as he will readily quote) 'the house and lineage of David' – that, of course, is *King* David. He can go way back beyond David, too, as he'll tell anyone willing to listen to the genealogical roll call. In fact, he claims to trace his family, via Jacob, Isaac and Abraham, to Adam himself – and thus to the Creator.

Despite his noble links with ancient royalty, there is nothing regal about Joseph's life when I first encounter him. It has, however, a firm and constant foundation; for, as well as being gratified by his antecedents, he is proud, too, of his skill as a carpenter.

Actually, 'carpenter' is far too demeaning a term for such a craftsman with wood whose calloused hands are adept with handsaw, chisel and plane, practised at the lathe, well-used to the placing of a nail, the wielding of a hammer.

Whilst furniture purchased from Joseph's workshop is plain, homely and functional, it has a simple grace, giving its presence in the home a certain artless beauty that sets it apart from the everyday.

But Joseph has his worries. He is no longer as young as he was — let say, for argument's sake, early-to-mid-thirties — and with no children, there's no one to carry forward those prized qualities of his life into future generations. As things stand, the reputation of Joseph the carpenter will die with him — or, indeed, long before that, as and when his eyesight and energies inevitably begin to wane and fail.

Nazareth, twelve miles southwest of the Sea of Galilee, is a village of little or no importance: if oral tradition is to be trusted, it has long been a common insult to ask whether anything good could ever come out of Nazareth. The locals including Joseph react to such slanders with indignation, as folks tend to do when others attack the place they call home. Apart from which, Nazareth is where Joseph meets Mary.

Maybe the encounter comes about through someone knowing someone else who is a cousin of a neighbour's friend (the circumstances are actually unimportant) and, although she a good few years his junior, his pulse misses a beat at her shy smile and his heart leaps and takes hope.

Perhaps it happens thus – by nature I am a romantic – but it may be that their eventual betrothal is a somewhat more practical agreement along the lines of a business transaction: an investment, by way of a dowry (carpentry provides a steady income) paid to Mary's parents – let's call them, in keeping with some accounts of men, Joachim and Anne – in exchange for a wife and a future mother of children.

However it comes about, they are duly betrothed. Plans are in hand for the wedding and their life together, when there falls upon this pleasant couple and their seemingly uncomplicated arrangement a mallet blow as heavy as any Joseph ever plied at his work. In the way that only a woman knows, even one who is young and innocent of much about the ways of the world, Mary knows that she is going to have a child.

And that is where I come in. Some have named me Gabriel, but the names men give us matter little. God knows who we are and that is enough. However, since Gabriel *is* a familiar name, I am happy to go by it for the telling of this tale.

You will understand now, perhaps, why I set little store by the outward looks of humankind: our way of looking is not yours. You look first at the outer and, only then, at what is within. Angels have to look from the inside out. That's how God arranged it; and, as far as I'm able to judge, it's more of an asset than a hindrance.

But to return to Joseph and his fiancée; they are overwhelmed by the unimaginable and divided by the inexplicable. Time, then to send in the angels; after all, they have a well-chronicled history as experts in the delicate job of making known the ways of God to man.

I need not repeat the story of my visitation to Mary: it has been immortalised by the greatest artists in the world and, despite my first-hand knowledge of the meeting, I will not quibble with any of their various interpretations. All that need concern us are the simple facts: a young girl, desperately fearful at first – it is not easy to accept the concept of a virgin birth, especially if you are the virgin – but then swiftly accepting, with a wisdom beyond her years, that what is to be will be; that she is to bear a son whose name has already been decreed as 'Jesus' and who is to be called the Son of the Most High.

No one should think that Mary's response – 'be it unto me according to thy word' – is easily said or, come to that, fully understood, but faith miraculously transports the impossible into the sphere of the feasible and makes viable the seemingly absurd.

As for her betrothed, it is not so straightforward. Joseph is a good man – I should, perhaps, have mentioned that earlier, but then you may already have guessed as much for yourself. If you were looking for a word to describe Joseph, you might settle on 'decent', 'honourable' or 'virtuous'. But, to my mind, 'good' is good enough, going as it does straight to the heart of the matter. And, being a good man, he has no wish to see Mary's young life destroyed by disgrace. The solution in Joseph's mind is obvious, however painful: an end to their betrothal by a discreet separation.

But that is not part of the plan. So, to use an archaic word another annunciation is called for. However, to tell a man that the young woman he was intending to marry is about to conceive a child that is from God and *is* God, is not easy for either of us.

Joseph's way of looking at the world is simple – do not misunderstand me, *he* is not *simple*, far from it – but he is uncomplicated, whereas my news is phenomenally complicated. His thoughts about religion are still pretty much what he had been taught as a child. His faith is humble, his expectations of God are modest and, like most people, he has zero previous experience of encountering angels.

It is recorded that I appeared to Joseph in a dream and that will do: meetings with angels are not that common – though maybe not as infrequent as you might at first suppose – and if rationalising the experience as a dream makes it seem a little less outlandish to the one visited, then where's the harm in that?

And, in any case, to think of Joseph as something of a dreamer only gives greater definition to his character; it suggests sensitivity and intuition, and aligns him with his ancestor and namesake whose story is told in the Book of Genesis and who was a noted dreamer of dreams.

Here I am, then, in the dream of this later Joseph, the carpenter from Nazareth ....

I have to say, for a man in a dream, he does a lot of pacing to and fro, asking questions that cannot be glibly answered, demanding explanations that require a degree more patience to understand than a man in his predicament is ready to give. It is a tussle that, for me, brings back centuries-old memories of a night of wrestling with one of his forebears, Jacob ....

Like many passionate personal discussions, it begins with the focus fixed on the pain of injustice, the wound of having been wronged, before moving on to the hurt of humiliation. But, as I've said, Joseph is a good man and, eventually, he finds a way to accommodate the possibility – and then accept the truth – of what I tell him: that Mary's child is the work of the Holy Spirit.

Naturally, he still wonders what exactly that means. Angels may understand and theologians hypothesise about the nature of such an entity, but for most people – including carpenters who are also good men – it is a real challenge.

But, by the time Joseph awakes from what he will later refer to as his dream, he has reached the conclusion that – although it is all still outside his full comprehension – he has somehow been caught up in a kind of divine intrusion into the history of the world that will reach farther than the farthest fields of Nazareth.

The outcome? Joseph will, as planned, take Mary as his wife and assume the responsibility of caring for a child he had not fathered.

In making this decision, however, he doesn't fully reckon with the local ramifications. When the news breaks, it is beyond shocking. In a parochial little town like Nazareth, conventional to its very roots, it is the all-consuming subject of gossip and speculation. Joseph's betrothed, young Mary, unblemished child of honourable and devout parents is – to use the discreet euphemism of the biblical translators – 'with child': out of wedlock and out of kilter with every right and decent rule of social propriety.

The depth and degree of the shame visited on these two families is profound. One question, whispered and muttered, is on everyone's lips. Who was responsible for this awkwardly premature pregnancy? Was it Joseph? After years of celibacy, had he too eagerly cast aside decorum and – like his ancestor, Adam – recklessly snatched what was not his to enjoy? Or had another stolen into the heart of the garden and, with the serpent's guile that seduced luckless Eve, plundered forbidden fruit?

But Joseph and Mary, boldly putting their faith in God and each other, get married and weather the storm; and, as is so often the way with tittle-tattling affairs, the outrage proves to be little more than a nine day's wonder.

It's true that, for a short while, the business of Nazareth's premier carpenter suffers a minor setback; but human pragmatism rises above most troubles and, eventually and necessarily, the need for a new table, chair or bed overtakes the tut-tutting expressions of disapproval.

Then comes a day when Mary receives unexpected family news and goes off, alone, to the hill country of Judah to visit her cousin Elizabeth. Despite Elizabeth being well past the age for bearing children, it emerges that she is also expecting a baby: a boy who will grow up to play a significant role in this story.

Meanwhile, Joseph, marvelling at the fact that miracles do not always come singly, concentrates on his daily tasks: cutting and sawing; making sturdy joints; vigorously smoothing surfaces and chiselling simple, honest decoration.

Mary is gone for several months, and, to better focus his mind on the coming event, Joseph works into his long, lonely evenings making a cradle for his future foster-son. It is finished and ready for Mary's inspection on her return. She gently caresses the wood and smiles her pride while Joseph glows his gratitude.

Whilst a fine token of mutual love and trust, that cradle – with a bitter-sweet irony – is destined to never be used. Powers mightier than a humble carpenter are at work, believing (as they always do) that they are pursuing their own agenda and so miss the reality that they are, in truth, merely part of a larger plan drawn by a greater architect.

So, although his part in this narrative is brief, it is time to cue the involvement of Gaius Octavius Thurinus, more commonly known as Augustus Caesar.

2
Nativity

'And it came to pass in those days, that there went out a decree from Caesar Augustus, that all the world should be taxed.' Doubtless that's how you've heard the story and I'm not going to waste time engaging with historians who carp about the veracity of this statement – after all, human memory is more transient than the life of a mayfly, as you will know if you've ever got to the top of a flight of stairs only to have forgotten why you climbed them.

So, to continue …

Eight months on from when we last met him, Joseph is sweeping wood-shavings and sawdust out of his workshop door. Since it is a mechanical task requiring little concentration, his thoughts are far away – well over ninety miles, or so he reckons – in Bethlehem. It is the city of his ancestor, King David, but he has never been there. Why would he? Travel ninety miles or more, for *what?*

But, like it or not, Bethlehem is where he now has to go, as required by Caesar Augustus, in order to be registered in a census! These Romans with all their confounded rules and regulations – *and taxes*!

Without realising he has done so, Joseph has stopped brushing. He can feel anxiety welling up and taking hold. It would be a bad enough journey at the best of times, but there is Mary: now in the last month of her first pregnancy. How is he to travel ninety miles with a wife who, at best, would find the journey arduous and who, at worst, might go into labour at any point along the way? Some men might have resented being in such a situation; might have asked, not unreasonably, why him? But, as you are by now aware, Joseph *isn't* 'some men'.

Instead, he seeks advice from an old woman who lives a few doors away and who took his side when the scandal first became public, solely on the principle that anyone who has everyone against them deserves at least one champion. She is a midwife and, when she was a young girl, had helped bring Joseph into the world and, years later, had done the same for Mary.

This no-nonsense, down-to-earth woman explains to this bachelor-minded married man the essential facts of life about giving birth, recommends that he ask a woman's help and tells him those things that an expectant mother needs to hear in order to get her through the ordeal.

Sending him off to pack what is needed for the journey, she adds – as if she were confident that her observations would be duly noted in high places – that if this baby really is *from God*, then God had better make pretty sure He is keeping an eye on things!

The house and workshop are shuttered and locked and Joseph settles Mary on the old donkey that has hitherto spent its weary life carrying the carpenter's tables and chairs to their new homes.

Forgive the interjection, but I need to say something about the donkey. I realise that this is superfluous because for hundreds of years the presence of the donkey has been taken for granted; understandably, since this much put-upon animal has been depicted as having a humble, but significant, role in the telling of this tale. But the truth is, there's no *official* basis for involving a donkey in the narrative other than a need to take a ninety-mile journey. Nevertheless, I'm glad that someone decided to give Mary a donkey to ride upon, if only because, one day, her as-yet-unborn son will also ride on a donkey towards his destiny.

You don't need to know much about Joseph and Mary's journey: the laborious daily slog along stony, dusty hill roads in stifling heat; the long, bitterly cold nights huddled by the roadside that pass with tedious slowness. Joseph gives up counting the days, needing no calendar other than Mary's changing condition. If they reach Bethlehem before the baby is born they will be lucky. And they are – although luck, of course, has nothing to do with it.

Night is descending and Mary's contractions are beginning as they trudge into the small town. The exhausted travellers find themselves hemmed in on all sides by milling crowds who either do not know where they are going or, if they do, are hopelessly lost.

Every town is a mystery to outsiders, and on this night, Bethlehem is full to capacity with outsiders. Joseph's worst fears are confirmed. The influx of those responding to mighty Caesar's edict are all looking for accommodation – and not finding it. At inn after inn they receive the same curt response that has since figured in hundreds of dramatic interpretations of this story: 'No room! No room!'

Then, beyond expectation, one innkeeper – perhaps on the insistence of his kind-hearted better-half – takes pity on the distracted traveller with a wife on the point of childbirth. To be sure, there's no room in the inn, but if they have nowhere else to go … well, then there is, at least, a stable …

Yes. We have now arrived at one of the most famous buildings – or, to be precise, *outbuildings* – in art and literature: the stable. But what can I possibly say of the place?

In your own mind you will have the perfect picture of exactly what it looked like, courtesy of Botticelli, Tintoretto, Caravaggio, Rubens, El Greco or a thousand others. It might be a rough-hewn cave or a rickety lean-to of wattle and thatch. I suggest, therefore, that just as you have always seen it in your mind's eye, is how you should see it now.

You may keep the lowing oxen, the braying donkey, the golden carpet of scattered straw illuminated by the light of a lantern, hanging from a beam. But add in, if you will, what the painters, out of piety or propriety, have tended to omit: the dirt, the anxiety, the pain, the sweat and the blood.

Add, too, the midwife who helps with the birth. In stories where she is mentioned, she is named Emea; and I am going to suggest — since I have mentioned her already — that she is that compassionate wife of the innkeeper, taking precious time from her responsibilities as hostess to bring a little food and wine, a calming voice, a reassuring touch and, most importantly, a bowl of hot water and some old — but *clean* — cloths with which to wash and wrap the new-born child.

As the midwife bustles back to her usual duties, the little family is left alone. Mary — despite her youth — is a life force to be reckoned with. The birth has been no harder for her than for many other first-time mothers, but she has brought her child into the world far away from the security of home and family and with only the faithful Joseph and a caring stranger to help. Now, despite the exhaustion of the journey and her labour, she is — like any new mother — totally absorbed in her baby. Joseph stands on the periphery of her experience, gazing with a mixture of wonderment and confusion at the child being rocked in Mary's arms.

Every father looks to see some semblance of himself in his child, but not Joseph. There is no similarity to seek. He tries to feel how he imagines he ought to feel, but the more he does so, the more he is aware that this child both is and, yet, is *not* his son. He has played no part in making him and yet this vulnerable little bundle is now his responsibility. If it was Mary's burden to bear this special child, then it is now his to learn to love it as if it were his own.

But how does any father set about loving a son, whether his own or, as here, by adoption? Everyone understands a mother's love, it is a given; a father's love is harder to define and, at this moment, Joseph has no idea how to begin.

Jesus, for so he is named – as preordained – has scarcely been cradled to sleep in the crude, straw-filled manger that has to substitute for Joseph's lovingly made crib left back in Nazareth, when a group of shepherds, plain and simple folk, come peeping into the scene. Awkward and hesitant, they talk in hushed astonishment of seeing an Angel of the Lord – I'm sure I don't need to name him – accompanied by a heavenly host bidding them to come to witness an event that, by its very ordinariness, is extraordinary.

They are followed, as is the way with shepherds, by a straggling flock of sheep. The youngest shepherd – no older than the boy David when he tended his father Jesse's sheep on these same hills – carries in his arms a new-born lamb, which he sets down at the foot of the manger. Obviously, for reasons of retrospective symbolism, there *has* to be a lamb …

For Joseph, the arrival of these strangers – unashamedly rough-and-ready men and boys from the fields outside town – is truly puzzling: why would God choose to announce the miraculous birth of his son to a bunch of shepherds rather than, say, the priests and religious officials? The obvious answer, which is the one Joseph sagely settles on, is that you have to start somewhere.

If you want a more sophisticated explanation for the shepherds' role in this drama, then it could be that they provide a telling link to David, the shepherd-king? Or that they signify that the child whose nativity this is will become, one day, a shepherd of men? Or, yet again, that they are there to provide a proletarian witness: the common man allowed to view the uncommon wonder that has taken place; just as the three kings – who are, even now, *en route* to this narrative – might be thought to represent the presence of the great and good, the wise and powerful?

Which, inescapably, brings us to those three notable figures …

3
Epiphany

$\mathcal{T}$ ime to talk about those Three Kings –
or, as they are alternatively known, the
Three Wise Men …

You have seen them so many times – in
their robes, crowns and turbans – that it will
not change your view to be told that the
number three is only a guess (based on the

number of gifts), that they were not necessarily kings (at least not until they were designated as such in much later versions of the story), that their names, as we now popularly know them, were never *officially* recorded and that they didn't actually arrive that night at the stable, but came later – up to *two years* later – long after Mary, Joseph and the child were living in rather more conventional accommodation.

But rather than confuse what has been a perfectly successful story that has stood the test of time for centuries, we'll stick to the facts as they have been set down in legend.

They come, these wise men from the East – sages, let's say, in their own far-off lands – with their camels, entourages, servants and all the standard paraphernalia of authority figures.

They are also sometimes referred to as Magi – 'magicians' is probably not the best word, so let's say they are 'astrologers', although they are also, almost certainly, astronomers since, in those times, the two are pretty much one and the same.

Men of stature and significance they may be, but they are certainly not followers of the

God of Moses. Nevertheless, they have been summoned to make their journey by the rising of a new star in the Eastern sky. There are those who have sought to explain this claim with speculations about comets and eclipses, but I prefer the more poetic explanation that the heavens themselves proclaimed the magnitude of this cosmic event.

The challenge set these Magi was to seek, find and pay reverence to a child who, as the signs foretold, was born to kingship. And, without doubt, it has proved a hard task and has been a long and onerous pilgrimage through the worst bleak mid-winter weather.

However, as their quest nears its goal, these wise men – for all their wisdom – make a disastrous and near-fatal error. They decide to consult the local monarch, King Herod (or, as he prefers, Herod the Great), as to the birthplace of the new sovereign of whom they've been told. It was, I suppose, the logical thing to do: if you are seeking the whereabouts of one king, ask the advice of another.

Unfortunately, this particular king happens to be a paranoid psychopath. So when three wandering sages ask the Jewish-born Herod, *'Where is the child born King of the Jews?'*, he is seriously rattled. What does it mean? Usurpation? Herod consults his own wise men and, from their extensive knowledge of ancient prophecy, they advise His Majesty that Bethlehem is the likely birthplace. Had Joseph been aware of this, several perplexing aspects of his recent experiences would have made more sense, such as that edict of Caesar Augustus and the ninety-mile trek to a Bethlehem birthplace. Order is all too often masked by partial knowledge.

The fearful Herod slyly instructs the travellers to pursue their mission and, if they find the child, to return with news so that – as he disingenuously claims – he, too, may go and pay homage. The unsuspecting Magi head straight to Bethlehem, unaware that the consequence of their regrettable mistake will cost many lives.

That is in the future; for the moment, here they are three more outsiders arriving in the heavily congested town. For the sake of continuity, then, let's return to that now somewhat overcrowded stable to witness their entrance. Out of courtesy to the old stories, I will use their traditional names …

Caspar (or, if you prefer, Kaspar or Gaspar), the young man: lithe, virile and clean-shaven, believed by some to be a king of India; Melchior, the old man: stooped and venerable with long white hair and beard, often referred to as a king of Persia; and Balthazar, bearded and dark of skin: a king, it is said, of Arabia. You can, if you've a mind to, research their individual and collective histories across centuries of lore, but – believe me – as with any fable it will add little to your appreciation.

They kneel or, in the case of Melchior (whose old knees no longer permit kneeling) bow before Mary and the baby, something so at odds with Joseph's understanding of custom and correctness that he steps back a pace in bafflement.

Then the visitors open and offer gifts of astonishing value and disconcerting significance that Mary accepts with solemnity and apparent understanding, but which further trouble Joseph and make him feel even more an observer of another person's story.

Caspar is first; his gift, enfolded in richly embroidered silk, is a porphyry jar, plain and unadorned, but with a stopper of blue agate which, when removed, releases the clean, sweet, aroma of frankincense that transforms the stale stable air with its bouquet of citrus and spice.

Melchior is next, his gift, securely tied with leather straps, is a finely wrought casket of antique silver, studded with garnets as red as blood and pearls the colour of a summer moon and, within, a great quantity of gold gleaming with a heavy, burnished warmth in the lantern-light.

Then last (or first, the order is unimportant) Balthazar presents his gift: a purple velvet bag secured with golden, tasselled cords from which he takes a box of pale, translucent alabaster incised with a complex design inlaid with lapis lazuli the colour of a peacock's breast. When opened, a heady, overpowering perfume spills out into the air: redolent of new-turned earth, laced with resin, it is the bitter fragrance of myrrh.

These offerings are not only heavy with weight and worth but also with prefigurement: frankincense representing divinity and worship; gold for kingship and honour; and myrrh for death and burial.

If Joseph has even a glimmer of comprehension about the meaning of these portents, it is overwhelmed by the prosaic question of how he will manage the journey back to Nazareth with wife, child and such seriously cumbersome luggage.

Before that, however, they have to travel a little over five miles to Jerusalem in order to fulfil the rituals of their faith.

Only five miles … no distance really … but still … those gifts *are* heavy …

4
The First Gift

J have described Joseph as a proud man: taking pride in his ancestry and in his skills as a carpenter, but I would also call him a humble man and, from my perspective, it was for that humility that he was chosen as a surrogate father for Mary's child.

Anyway, once the Magi have departed

— having disrupted everyone's lives in the way all Very Important People tend to do, intentionally or not — Joseph pushes aside the troubling questions teeming through his brain and, instead, sets about finding a solution to his most immediate problem: what to do about the gifts the visitors have left behind.

Although their worth is unimaginable to Joseph, he understands that they represent a potential danger to his family — who knows what rogues and vagabonds might lay in wait for the unwary traveller carrying such items of rare value on a deserted stretch of road?

Borrowing some old timber and a few tools from the innkeeper, Joseph makes a box to hold the precious gifts and this he hides in an old sack that had once held cattle feed.

That done and while packing these treasures for the journey to Jerusalem, he occasionally fidgets about what meaning they might have. After all, they were hardly the kind of presents one would think of giving a baby! Then it occurs to him that perhaps he and Mary were meant to *do* something with the gifts? But, if so, *what?*

Eventually, being the humble man he is, he decides that, if and when the time comes, they will probably know what is to be done.

The family arrive in Jerusalem, forty days after the birth of the child – an event referred to by Bible historians as 'The Presentation in the Temple'. You might suppose that Joseph is, by now, used to curious happenings, but each one seems to come crashing into his world with earthquake force and what happens on this particular day is no exception.

The Temple … Just how much do you need to know about this place? Its design and construction is complex and laden with all manner of symbolism, as is the ritual that Mary and Joseph have come here to fulfil. If that's potentially interesting to you then, by all means, go and find a good reference source and read all about it. It is interesting, no question; but, right now, I need to press ahead with my story. So, suffice it to say that, for Joseph and Mary, who have been there before, the Temple is an awe-inspiring – if a somewhat intimidating – place that lies at the very heart of the history and beliefs of their people.

The age-old rituals are being observed; the priests are serving the holy laws and ministering to the people, intoning the necessary prayers and offering the required sacrifices, the air clouded with incense. Mary carries the child while Joseph shoulders their belongings including the heavy sack containing the gifts of the Magi.

Everything, as is right and proper, is done in due manner. As required by scripture, Joseph pays for the appropriate sacrifice and, the cost of a lamb being beyond his means, their offering is the cheaper option of two turtle doves. It's a trifling expense, but not one without cost to a family with little money and miles from home.

Then from out of the throng, an old man approaches. Although bent and crumpled with age, his eyes blaze with the exuberance of a man half his age. Mary and Joseph are stopped in their tracks by his advance and the fact that he is reaching out with his wizened, hands as if to take the child from Mary's arms.

Surprised by the suddenness of the act, Joseph automatically steps forward to interpose himself – no doubts in his mind right now about the role of fatherhood – only to be pre-empted as Mary, clearly uncertain and yet oddly calm, hands her son into the old man's care.

Once again, Joseph feels that harsh sense of disconnection with reality: yet another stranger, with seemingly some knowledge and interest in his wife and baby, is intervening in his once-so-simple life. There he stands, this old man, wedged between them and gazing at the child with a rapt and euphoric expression that Joseph identifies as some kind of unexplained joy but which, in truth, is closer to ecstasy.

Time to introduce this interloper: Simeon, a faithful, god-fearing man who believes that he has received the divine assurance that – despite being a good age – he will not die until he has seen the coming of the one who is destined to be the saviour of the world. It is that belief that has brought him into the Temple on this very day.

I realise that, for some, the fact that he instantly knows that this baby is the one he is waiting for is yet another mystery in a story already laden with mysteries, but knowing what I know about how these things work, this seems feasible enough.

So, here's Simeon and he's about to speak words that have survived across the years and are still rather obscurely referred to by the Latin tag, 'Nunc dimittis'. If you've ever come across them, you'll probably also be aware that they've been endlessly set to music – one recording, I'm told, even briefly made it into something called the Top Ten. I say, 'I'm told', because, on occasions, angel knowledge can be rather hazier than you might expect. But I digress …

Inevitably, Simeon's words have become rather detached from the circumstances in which they were originally spoken and, via the so-called skill of modern translators, have lost most of their poetry. So, for that reason, I'm quoting the words in the form in which they've been known for a goodly length of human time.

Staring intently into the child's eyes with tears in his own, Simeon says in a voice with a strength that belies his years: *'Lord, now lettest thou thy servant depart in peace, according to thy word: for mine eyes have seen thy salvation, which thou hast prepared before the face of all people.'*

Simeon's pronouncement stills the hubbub in the Temple. He goes on: *'A light to lighten the Gentiles and the glory of thy people Israel.'*

Throughout, the child, with a serious look on his little face, returns Simeon's steady gaze.

There are murmurs among worshippers: why is the old man talking about non-Jews — here, in the Temple — and in the same sentence in which he mentions the people of Israel? Some laugh at what they take for an old man's ramblings; others smile sympathetically, shake their heads or make that circular movement of the forefinger at the side of the head that is a universal gesture of perceived craziness. But the moment passes and the hustle and bustle of the Temple traffic resumes.

In Joseph's experience, over the last few weeks, Mary has always been composed – regardless of how unusual, or even bizarre, the circumstances – but, today, her expression mirrors his own bewilderment.

Then Simeon speaks again: this time directly to Mary and Joseph, blessing them and giving them a message that – by its unfathomable nature – only serves to increase their apprehension. In a calm voice, that heightens the profundity of what he says, he talks of their baby as having come into the world as a warning sign that would cause some to stand firm but many others to fall.

Finally, gazing into Mary's eyes alone with a sudden, fierce intensity, Simeon tells her that motherhood will one day bring her such suffering as if a thrusting sword had pieced her very soul.

This thought is so unexpected and so deeply shocking that Mary is overwhelmed in a moment of unexplained terror and anticipated grief. An involuntary tremor runs through her body and Joseph instinctively draws a shielding arm around her, as if to guard her from such a fearful foreshadowing.

Her protector scans the crowd of faces, anxiously looking for one he recognises – *mine*. Seeking the eyes of that angel from his dream, wanting to ask why nothing had been said before about swords piercing and thrusting.

You might think, perhaps, that I could have done more to warn them, alerted them to the fact that their child's future – and theirs – is to be marked by conflict, pain and sorrow. But that's the way with angelic intrusions into human affairs. It is rather like two people trying to have a conversation in an uncommon language: it is difficult to move beyond broad concepts into details and subtleties.

Failing to recognize me in the crowd – although I am standing at his shoulder, just as I stand close to you now – Joseph returns his gaze to Simeon, but the old man is silent now, his long-awaited epiphany realised.

However, this disturbing episode has a coda. There's a murmur of urgent female voices and an elderly woman comes slowly forward to join the group. Taking the child from Simeon, she tenderly cradles him in her arms, looking at him with her pale, rheumy eyes.

As Saint Luke tells it, she is a widow named Anna and is of a great age: at least eighty-four years old. Well-known to regular Temple-goers, she is to be found there every day, worshipping and praying. More than that, among the women – and even some of the men – she is considered something of a prophetess: a reputation confirmed by the fact that she now endorses what Simeon has just foretold.

The thing is, whilst Luke thoughtfully provides details of her ancestry (she is the daughter, he tells us, of Phanuel of the tribe of Asher), he frustratingly omits to record what she actually says. I'll leave you to make your own conclusions about why historians have a habit of favouring the wisdom of men over that of women.

Fortunately for us, we can consult the work of a number of mediaeval artists who have depicted Anna as holding an unrolled scroll bearing the words we now hear her speak: 'My heart hath rejoiced … Blessed is the womb that bore thee … This child created Heaven and Earth …'

The devout women of her acquaintance understand this astonishing claim and are soon passing it on to anyone who will listen. The incredulous enigma: creator self-created as a child; or, as you still sing in your Christmas carol, 'Offspring of a virgin's womb, veiled in flesh the Godhead see'.

Their scene in this celestial drama done, Simeon and Anna slip away into the crowd and Joseph and Mary, alone once more with their child, cling to one another, struggling to decipher what has just occurred.

They are suddenly wrenched back from their confused thoughts by the pitiful bleat of a lamb being slaughtered and the smell of fresh-spilled blood. In that very moment, they are suddenly fully conscious of a mystical concept that has since tested some of the greatest human intellects: that God is intervening in history – past, present and future – by entering the world as both priest and sacrifice.

Just as those who have spent many years in each other's company will sometimes voice the same thought at the precisely the same time, so in an instant of mutual but unspoken understanding and agreement, Mary and Joseph arrive at a decision.

Here, in this holy place, symbolising the centuries-long relationship between God and man – here where the priest on behalf of man enters into the very presence of the Creator – it is time to give up one of the Magi's gifts.

Unshouldering the heavy sack, Joseph unties the neck and pulls out a package swathed in richly embroidered silk. The priest looks on questioningly, as Joseph unwraps a porphyry jar, plain and unadorned but with a stopper of blue agate.

Caspar's gift …

With another glance towards Mary, as if seeking her confirmation, Joseph hands over the jar of rare frankincense to accompany their humble sacrifice of two small birds.

As the perfume is poured onto the fire, releasing its sweet, heady aroma, the priest and those nearby who have caught a glimpse of a small but uncommon moment of drama, wonder how a couple, so clearly poor, could have come by so rich a gift.

Only Joseph and Mary – and, perhaps, old Simeon and Anna, watching from somewhere in the crowd – realise the significance of such a priestly offering made on behalf of a little child, rising like a scented prayer and engulfing the Temple.

Time now, thinks Joseph to return to Nazareth, to pursue his honest trade, care for his wife and raise their son. But it is not to be – or, at least not yet.

You remember the crazed despot, Herod the Great? While everything I've been relating was going on, he has been waiting with mounting agitation for the return of the Wise Men. However, the Magi have smartly outmanoeuvred his murderous intent. Did I mention that they had been warned – yes, in another dream – to return to their homes by an alternative route? Well, they were and they have. And when Herod realises that he has no way of finding and destroying the child-who-would-be-king, he embarks on a homicidal spree, destined to live in infamy as 'The Massacre of the Innocents'.

Thousands of children throughout his kingdom, aged two and under, are put to the sword, but despite the horrific and devastating consequences, Herod fails to reach the target of his fear and rage.

Why? Because, following another conversation with my friend Joseph, he agrees — to what would be the astonishment of anyone other than an angel — to take Mary and the baby and flee into Egypt and remain there until I tell him that it is safe to return.

Poor Joseph: another disruption of his once-so-ordered life; another long, wearisome journey toward an uncertain future. Loading up the donkey once more with Mary, their son and their bags and baggage (including the two remaining gifts) he heads off to that historic destination for exiles — the land of palms and pyramids — in search of a temporary home, casual work and, hopefully, safety.

5
The Second Gift

*T*wo years on, I give Joseph the news of Herod's death and the family finally set out for their home in Nazareth. It has been a long and anxious absence and has brought with it trials and tribulations that Joseph could never have anticipated, all of which he has borne with no little humility and great patience, determined to do what was right for his wife and child.

Before going on, I have to admit that – from the perspective of a human – there is precious little information about the early years of Jesus' life. For example, take the statement: *'And the child grew, and waxed strong in spirit, filled with wisdom: and the grace of God was upon him.'* You may find that a satisfactory resume or you may not.

It would, I feel, be helpful for mortals to have a version of these stories with a few additional angelic annotations; but, since that is not an option, you'll need to make do with what you have. So, maybe think about it in this way: if everything that you'd like to know was actually *known*, then there'd be no need for faith. And by the way, just to be clear, I'm not asking you to accept anything *I* say as 'gospel', but simply as an invitation to think in the spaces between paragraphs, sentences – sometimes, even, between *words*.

What follows next, then, is an example of thinking between one story and another; and, as such, you are free to take it or leave it.

So …

The baby grows – as babies do! Joseph returns to his carpentry and, between making items for the locals of Nazareth, he makes toys for his son. One day, when the child is playing on the floor of the workshop – pushing a little wooden horse and cart through the wood chips and plane-shavings – he suddenly gave a sharp cry, less in pain than surprise. Dropping his tools, Joseph rushes to see what has happened. There the child stands looking in wonderment at a spot of bright vermillion glistening in the palm of one of his little hands.

Kneeling down and rummaging through the shavings, Joseph finds the culprit: a large, bent nail that he had pulled from an old piece of wood earlier that day. Curiously there are no tears, but the child goes on intently studying the small wound with great curiosity. Distressed and perplexed, Joseph sweeps the boy into his arms, clutching him tight to comfort him or, perhaps, in the vain hope of protecting him against some suffering yet to come.

Just in case you think that this little tale

about the child having an accident with a nail in the workshop is pure fancy – and I'm not saying it isn't – there was a famous painter who depicted just such a scene, although slightly differently from how I have recounted it. You may have seen the picture … This artist, incidentally, was part of a movement known as the Pre-Raphaelites: a term I find rather amusing, knowing, as I do, Raphael himself – the archangel I mean, not the painter.

But, I'm deviating from my story …

There is one very specific recorded reference to Jesus' childhood that takes place when he is twelve.

Mary and Joseph with a contingent of friends and relations travel to Jerusalem in order to celebrate Passover. After the festival, the party is heading back to Nazareth and has been on the road for a day when Mary and Joseph suddenly realise that Jesus isn't among the other young people. Consternation!

Naturally, there are anxious enquiries: who saw him last, when and where? Followed by all those predictable responses that inevitably go with people trying to be helpful while actually only adding to the level of concern. Then out of the confusion there's someone who thinks that, maybe, the last time the boy was seen was back in Jerusalem …

Simultaneously cross and worried, Joseph and Mary have no choice but to retrace their steps and head back to the city while the rest of the party continue with their journey.

Back in the city – and Jerusalem is a big city – their next dilemma is where to start looking? Having to start somewhere, they do what you would do: they ask anyone and everyone. *Have you seen a twelve-year-old boy wandering around by himself?*

It's an obvious question that, repeatedly, gets an obvious answer. Yes, of course people have seen a boy who might easily be twelve – or perhaps eleven – or possibly thirteen! In a city that size there are bound to be hundreds of boys around that age.

Some, stopping long enough to read the apprehension and distress in Mary and Joseph's faces, ask what he looks like, this boy? The parents try to give a description; but, frankly, they could be describing anyone's child.

And so the search goes on. For three exhausting days, Mary and Joseph traipse every street, alley and passageway, checking and double-checking every gate and marketplace. Becoming increasingly fraught, anxious and angry, they start out – in the way humans usually do – by blaming each other only to end up reproaching themselves.

Then, finally, an old man sitting on the flight of steps leading up to the Temple offers a shred of hope: there was a boy, he tells the fretful parents, an astonishing youngster … *Astonishing?* Well, yes, that could be him, couldn't it? The next question, obviously, is where *is* this astonishing child?

Indicating the way up the stairs, the old man tells them that the boy is where he's been every day for the last three days – in the Temple. And that's exactly where they find him: sitting in the Temple Courts, among a group of distinguished scholars and venerable teachers – a twelve-year-old boy asking and answering questions that are so uncommon, so mature, so challenging that the learned men are incredulous.

The earnest discussion between the boy and the elders comes to an abrupt end with the frantic arrival of Joseph and Mary. Even before anything is said, their frustration, fury and relief are a palpable presence.

Joseph may have intended to be the first to speak but, instead, it is his wife – perhaps to prevent him saying too much, too hastily; although her own response is hardly muted. *'Child'*, Mary asks, *'why have you treated us like this?'* Hot tears are stinging in her eyes.

Wounded on account of her hurt, Joseph again moves to say *his* piece. Authority and discipline are his responsibility, as father, aren't they? But, again, it is Mary who speaks for him, for both of them, remonstrating with a sharpness that has more to do with sadness than wrath: *'Your father and I have been searching for you everywhere, out of our minds with worry.'*

Then the calm reply, the small voice echoing in the now otherwise hushed courtyard: *'Why were you searching for me?'* the child asks, genuinely curious, trying to understand. *'Didn't you know I had to be in my Father's house and about my Father's business?'*

The parents cannot comprehend what he means. Unsurprisingly. How can they? His father is *right there*, beside his mother; his 'father's house' and his 'father's business' is a carpenter's shop in Nazareth … isn't it?

Having no reply to Jesus' seemingly inexplicable answer, the family leave the Temple in silence and set off once more for home. Even though nothing more is said, a vast cloud of unasked questions hovers over and between them. Saint Luke recounts Mary as keeping all these things in her heart. It's a common misconception that there is a maternal prerogative to such activity, so don't discount the idea of Joseph doing his own fair share of pondering.

You see, there's a compact that exists between most fathers and sons. A man, unless he has reason to think otherwise, accepts that he is the biological father of the child to whom his partner has given birth. Similarly, the child accepts that the man he has always been told is his father is just that.

But in the instance of Joseph and Jesus there is no such compact. Joseph has known from the outset that he was not the father of the child; instead he was called upon to play the role of a father. What Joseph has been totally unprepared for is the revelation that Jesus not only knows that Joseph is *not* his father, but that he also knows who *is*!

Those reporting these things have said that Jesus returned to Nazareth with Joseph and Mary and 'was obedient to them' and that, for Joseph, is the most baffling aspect of this whole episode: the notion of God in human form being obedient to a mere man. But then the idea of Incarnation is complicated enough, even if you are not the adopted father to the one who is incarnate.

The term used by theologians for the period following the Jerusalem Temple incident is the 'Unknown Years of Jesus' or the 'Missing', 'Silent' or 'Lost' years. There are some pretty esoteric theories, such as the suggestion that he went to India or studied with a contemplative sect in the desert near the Dead Sea; or, again, that he travelled to Britain with Joseph – as alluded to in that verse beginning: 'And did those feet in ancient time walk upon England's mountains green'.

Without wanting to pour cold water on such beguiling stories, the truth, as you would suppose, is more prosaic: with Jesus spending the next eighteen years following his earthly father's chosen trade and becoming a carpenter.

That being the case presents a challenge to some generally held perceptions of Jesus' physical appearance. Rather than the beautiful, slight-framed figure afloat in a thousand stained-glass windows, I see a young man strengthened by hard work: his muscular arms toughened from lifting and carrying; his hands seasoned by the daily use of axe, saw and plane; and with old scars from splinter and nail and an occasional slip of the chisel.

Interestingly, there is a painting, seriously over-romanticised but stuffed with symbolism (by another of those Pre-Raphaelite fellows), depicting the young Jesus stretching after the effort of working at the sawhorse and casting an ominous cruciform shadow on the wall of his father's carpentry-shop. Of course, I realise a work of art isn't evidential, but artists quite often have a knack – and the freedom – for depicting truths.

How, then, did these years play out for the gradually aging Joseph? It would have been strange if he had not been pleased to see the way in which the boy, whom he now thought of as his own, had grown into youth and manhood; or to feel a sense of pride in his aptitude for the craft in which he had instructed him. This was what he had always wanted, longed for: someone who would carry on his trade and his reputation. The business of 'Joseph the Carpenter' was now 'Joseph and Son, Carpenters of Nazareth'.

I need to backtrack a little here – because otherwise I'll be accused of misleading you – to explain that the account of Mary and Joseph finding the twelve-year-old Jesus in the Temple is the last time Joseph makes an actual appearance in authorised scripture. This inexplicable void in the story that subsequently unfolds has been explained – to the perfect satisfaction of most of those who've ever wondered about it – by the supposition that sometime over the next few years, Joseph died.

Although, maddeningly, there are no actual details of his demise there are various stories, for example, that being very old at the time of his marriage to Mary – ninety years of age, according to some – Joseph died long before his foster son began fulfilling his world-changing calling.

But, if Joseph were, say, only somewhere in his sixties, then there ought to be more to his story …

This, then is *my* telling of that story …

Joseph, working alongside the young man who is following his own lifetime's task of shaping wood to meet the craftsman's will, finds that the odd and disturbing events from so many years earlier begin to fade in the day-to-day, year-in-year-out routine of family life.

Measuring his days, as he does, by a succession of sturdy, reliable, chairs and tables, beds and chests, ladders and doors, he is totally unprepared for the moment when all the confusing unexpectedness of thirty years before comes abruptly flooding back into his and Mary's life.

It begins, at first, at a distance. John, that unexpected son of Mary's aged cousin, Elizabeth, has recently become the subject of widespread interest that starts out as little more than curiosity.

Dressing outlandishly in camel skins held together by a leather belt, John is rumoured to be following an ascetic existence, living in the wild on honey and fruits.

But John's reputation rapidly grows into a combustible mix of fame and notoriety. He is now a firebrand preacher referred to as 'the Baptist' or 'the Baptizer', calling people to repent of their wrongdoings and to be washed clean of their sins by submitting to total immersion in the waters of the River Jordan.

It is late one morning when Joseph comes into the empty, silent workshop. He has been feeling tired lately and has taken longer than usual to get himself going at the beginning of the day. This has never been a problem, because Jesus has always been there, ahead of him, pushing on with whatever job they have in hand at the time. But, today, he is not there.

Joseph finds Mary and can tell, at once, that she is anxious …

She knows the reason for her son's absence and is clearly conflicted by what it means. When she tells Joseph that Jesus has gone to where his cousin is preaching to the crowds gathered on the banks of Jordan, he is similarly perturbed.

They are more bewildered when, a day or two later, one of their neighbours (who knew someone who had witnessed the encounter) describes how John had baptised Jesus along with all his other converts that day.

Joseph and Mary search back through their memories to everything I divulged to them, thirty years before, and begin asking what it was that they'd failed to understand. If Jesus was who they had been told he was – and if all those disconcerting signs that had attended his birth were true – then why would he need to be baptised into the new, cleansed life that John was preaching?

Their incomprehension is unwittingly endorsed when their informant confides that *his* informant told him that John had, at first, refused to baptise Jesus, saying that he wasn't worthy enough to even stoop down and unfasten Jesus' sandals.

At the time, I could only sympathise with them: Joseph and Mary – and, I might add, John – just as you can doubtless empathise with their uncertainty. Grappling with an enigma such as Incarnation is never easy.

Two more days have passed and Jesus has not returned. Another day follows, and another and another …

More stories reach their ears: someone saying that somebody else had said that another person who was there at the baptism had heard a voice, as if coming from heaven, saying something quite extraordinary about Jesus.

Here, for you (and the record), I'll just add the verbatim version of what was said by that voice: *'This is my Son, the Beloved, in whom I am well pleased.'*

'Son', thinks Joseph, when he hears this. Son? Those old puzzlements are back again. Whose son? Which father?

Forty days pass … I ought to point out,

here, that for 'forty days' you could read 'a significant period of time', rather like the forty days and nights of rain before Noah's ark was afloat, or the forty years of wandering in the wilderness …

And, indeed, as you might recall, during the forty days we're now talking about, Jesus was similarly alone in a desert wilderness of his own.

However long he was actually gone from his home and family – and whether that wilderness was a real place or a state of mind – it was long enough to give Joseph and Mary anxious days and sleepless nights.

Then, suddenly, he is back; weary and hungry, but seemingly changed by an inner transcendence that defies description. However, in another sense – very real and yet difficult to pin down – he is *not* back …

It would be natural for his parents to ask questions: Where have you been? And why? And didn't you think, like the last time you did this, that we would be worried half to death? But, perhaps recalling that very incident in the Temple all those years before, they choose not to ask.

As far as Joseph is concerned, it seems to him that Mary no longer needs to ask any questions – as though she already has a clear acceptance of the fact that their lives and the life of their son will never be the same again.

On the day of his return, Mary fusses around: fetching water with which to wash his hands and feet; bustling back and forth, preparing and delivering a meal.

But Joseph, escaping, wanders away into the workshop: his refuge, the place where, being surrounded by those things he has known and understood all his life, he always feels secure.

He knows now that he has to let go of his dream of a son who would continue to use the saws and chisels he has lovingly cleaned, sharpened and oiled for years and who might have carried on his trade — his father's business …

As these thoughts run through his head, he mechanically does what he has done countless times before: tidying up, stacking wood, putting away his tools, closing the vice, brushing down the workbench and sweeping the floor clean of chippings and shavings.

He pauses – he increasingly suffers from backaches now – and is suddenly aware of a scent that he has lived with for so many years that it is something he has almost ceased to notice: the fresh, clean, resinous smell of chopped, sawn, cut and planed wood. He inhales deeply with closed eyes, as if desperate to retain the fragrance in his memory and then turns and leaves the workshop knowing that neither he nor his son — Mary's son — God's son … will ever work there again.

Time runs sluggishly on awhile and then the stroke: unexpected and, yet, almost the equivalent of Joseph's silent resignation or abdication from the role of fatherhood. Month on month pass, he is slow to recover, as if he were painfully aware that his role in a story – which, in some ways, he only vaguely comprehends – is moving towards an end.

In the official documents, if I can describe them as such, the Joseph file is already closed. But in this telling of the tale, he has yet a part to play …

Events begin crowding together now. First, there's a family wedding in a village in Galilee; the invitation comes, but Joseph is not well enough to go; Mary attends, accompanied by Jesus, and returns with an extraordinary account of how the wine ran out – shame of shames for any wedding party – but how as a result of an intervention by Jesus, water is miraculously transformed into wine.

Next, with Jesus now rarely at home, a succession of stories and anecdotes about him make their way back to Nazareth and reach Joseph's ears: sometimes passed on to him with incredulous amazement, at other times recounted with cynical disbelief …

Stories about how a motley group of followers – among them fishermen and a tax collector – have gathered around his son, hanging on his every word, giving up their professions to travel with him here and there around the area of Galilee …

There are tales of miraculous happenings for which he is alleged to be, in some way, responsible: the diseased cured; the lame walking; the blind recovering their sight …

Then there are reports of the thoughts and words that he shares with the vast crowds that flock to hear him teach and preach: vaguely revolutionary messages, that speak of the blessedness of the poor, the meek and the hungry …

Joseph hears so many of these accounts that being the good man that we know him to be, he learns to listen to the words rather the tone and manner in which they are passed on, sifting the grains of wisdom from the chaff of reporting …

'Love your enemies and do good to them, and lend without any hope of return. You will have a great reward, and you will be children of the Most High …'

'Give, and there will be gifts for you: a full measure, pressed down, shaken together, and overflowing, will be poured into your lap; because the standard you use will be the standard used for you …'

And it is through this process of sieving and winnowing that Joseph begins to understand what his foster son meant in saying he had to be about his Father's business.

Weighing the words that reach his ears, an

itch develops in the old man's heart that grows and grows and demands to be scratched …

'Do not store up treasures for yourselves on earth, where moth and woodworm destroy and thieves break in and steal. But store up treasures for yourselves in heaven … For where your treasure is, there will your heart be too.'

One day, Mary finds her husband sitting pensively in the now abandoned workshop. In front of him on the bench, the leather strappings undone, is a finely wrought casket of antique silver, studded with garnets and pearls. The lid stands open revealing a gleaming stash of golden coins.

The second gift …

It has been secretly stored away, wisely guarded, prudently looked after for thirty years: a great treasure hidden in a humble carpenter's shop.

Why had they been keeping it, Joseph wonders? Had it been 'put by', to use one of your common sayings, 'for a rainy day'?

However, as he contemplates what is to him great wealth, Joseph isn't thinking about such questions. He knows the answer: like all three gifts given those thirty years ago it was simply a matter of waiting until the time was right, until that moment when – as with the frankincense – they would know what they were to *do* with the gift.

Taking Mary's hands in his, Joseph, can feel both her tenderness and her strength; looking into her eyes, he sees her love and her constancy. In that second of unity, they make their decision. Resolve what is to be done.

It is impossible for Joseph to make the journey and he will not permit Mary to undertake it alone. So a neighbour who is travelling to Galilee carries a message and, shortly afterwards, one of the disciples comes to visit.

Let's say, for the sake of this story, that the disciple is John – not the cousin, the Baptist, who is now awaiting death in Herod's prison, but the other one: often described as the disciple whom Jesus loves. This would be fitting since, one day, it will fall to this John to care for Mary as if she were his own mother.

To him Joseph and Mary entrust the precious gift so that it may be used wherever Jesus' disciples encounter need: food for the hungry, shelter for the homeless, clothes for the naked, medicine for the sick, common comforts for the prisoner.

The deed is done. Only one gift now remains.

6
The Third Gift

J oseph is fretful; he lies on his bed, drifting in and out of awareness, unsure if he is remembering or hallucinating. Over two years have passed since he and Mary surrendered Melchior's gold. Being now very ill, he understands, in his lucid moments, that the journey of his life is leading him inexorably towards the valley of the shadow of death. Obviously, such a presentiment is one with which angels have a problem empathising, but for Joseph (as for most humans) the concept of death had once been as remote as the farthest of far-off countries, whereas now it was no more than a street or two away.

His breathing on this particular day is shallow and rasping, his brow is damp with fever and he struggles to keep his eyes open and his thoughts clear.

Sometimes, recollections from the past come drifting up to him and he thinks, perhaps, he understands and everything makes sense, but then they always slip away again as sleep takes him.

He fleetingly recalls that day, not so long back, when Jesus returned to Nazareth and spoke in the synagogue, angering the town folk by implying that he was the fulfilment of ancient, sacred prophecies of a coming Saviour. After all, who was this Jesus? A person of no importance, the son of the local carpenter – in fact, as the old gossips remembered, someone of questionable parentage. In a fury, the congregation had dragged Jesus from the synagogue.

Joseph tosses in delirium, recalling the angry sound of the ruckus in the street outside the room where he lay bedridden … He sees again Mary rushing out of doors, her terror as she watches their neighbours – incandescent in their outrage – pursuing her son to the precipitous edge of a hillside from which they plan to cast him down … He experiences afresh the feelings of uselessness, that his own weak body prevents him from being what duty dictates that he should be – protector to his wife and son …

Then the memory of the curious reports of Jesus' miraculous escape; and, afterwards, the discussions about whether it was any longer safe for him and Mary to continue living in Nazareth, leading to the agonising decision to move away and go to live near family in Capernaum …

Silent tears accompany the memory of their emotional farewell to their home and

Joseph's workshop of so many years; and then the painful and disorientating journey …

Now another memory is swirling through his fevered brain, not one personally witnessed but vividly real, nevertheless, because he remembers how animatedly Mary recounted it: a day of astonishing adulation with Jesus entering Jerusalem like a triumphant king – although (and here he wonders if he isn't getting muddled) riding on a donkey rather than a more noble steed …

Then he is abruptly aware that it is now *this* particular day …

This *Friday* …

Mary is there with him, kneeling at his bedside, gently sponging his face and hands, feeding him a little (he is really too weary to eat), adjusting the pillow, smoothing the sheet. At the same time she is also *not* there – just as Jesus had returned home from the wilderness and, yet, at the same time, had never come back.

He searches her face – older and more careworn but still as beautiful to him as the day when he first saw her smile – there is some deep mystery unfolding in her mind and heart that he cannot fathom, cannot reach or name.

A vague recollection suddenly intrudes, a remembrance of murmured conversations between Mary and John, that nice young friend of Jesus, who still comes to visit them now and again …

There were hushed references, he recalls, to events that seem to have been happening over the last few days or, perhaps, only a matter of hours … *Which is it?* He is not sure, but he retains the troubling details …

Betrayal … priests … soldiers … arrest … accusations … a trial … and, yes … *yes* … judgement and sentence …

Joseph desperately struggles to put all these insistent fragments into some meaningful context involving his son …

Then, having cared for her husband, Mary leaves the house with a fierce urgency that fills Joseph with an unspeakable fear.

There was something that he once knew … something foretold – if he could only remember …

The house is very quiet now, with Mary gone.

This house … But it isn't *his* house, is it …? That was in Nazareth … That was some other time … long ago …

And it's not that other house in Capernaum either … No, this is *Jerusalem*, isn't it? *Yes* … But why are they living *here?*

Tumbling again into sleep, Joseph is back in that house in Nazareth, hearing the sounds with which it had once been filled: the rasping rhythm of sawing wood and the hammering tempo of mallet on joint; the singing of his young wife, the gurgling laughter of a little child …

When he awakes, everything is dark … dark as night …

What woke him? A searing flash of lightning violently illuminates the room for an instant before everything is plunged once more into blackness.

Then the ominous rumble and mighty crash of thunder and the sound of a rushing wind that rattles the doors and thumps at the shutters, followed by the incessant pummelling of rain upon the roof.

What *time* is it? Where is *Mary?*

Next a low, muffled growl as a tremor takes hold of the earth, seizes the building and Joseph's aching body and shakes them mercilessly. Outside: falling masonry and terrified screams …

What does it mean? Is it the end of all things that he had heard spoken of in readings from the holy word?

Then a sudden, fearful silence, so unfathomable and void that Joseph is acutely aware of the irregular beating of his heart before exhaustion drags him down once more into a wildly troubled nightmare.

Time passes: hours maybe – an eternity it seems.

Joseph doesn't need to open his eyes when Mary enters the room; he senses not just her presence but also the excruciating depth of her pain and grief. Simultaneously they both give a soft, shuddering sigh that hangs, sorrowing, in the air. Only then does Joseph look at her, dreading what he will see and, seeing it, feels a tear trickle across the dry, craggy terrain of his face.

For the first time in months, Joseph comprehends with an agonising clarity. He takes in, with the merest glance, her blood-stained dress, face and hands and it is as if he had seen her at the foot of the cross, cradling the broken body of her son – *their* son – just as she had nursed the new-born child all those years before in that Bethlehem stable …

Only then does Mary open one clenched fist to show the cruel iron nails that she is holding out for him to see. Joseph looks at them, takes one and scrutinises it as if – despite a lifetime's labour – he has never truly seen a nail before.

Hadn't there been an occasion, back in that other house in Nazareth, when a little child, playing on the sawdust-strewn floor of a carpentry shop, had cut his tiny hand on a nail and, whilst he had not cried at the sharpness of the pain, had showed a sense of astonished wonder that a bead of red could have blossomed in the middle of his small palm? Hadn't he gathered the child into his arms, wanting to comfort him, protect him from harm? Hadn't that been his role; what he was chosen to do? If so, then he had failed, for now it was too late – far too late – to shield and guard the child-become-man.

Turning his gaze again to Mary he saw in her expression of numb acceptance the fulfilment of the words of Simeon, the old man in the Temple, over twenty years ago … It has happened as foretold: Mary's soul has been pierced, as if by a thrusting sword … And so, too, has his …

Joseph registers the unasked question in his wife's reddened eyes that are now beyond crying.

Mary rises from his bedside and crosses to an old chest – more of a crate – that had been carried from Bethlehem to Egypt and back to Nazareth and then on to Capernaum and, later, to here …

Opening the battered, makeshift box, Mary withdraws a bag of purple velvet and unties the golden cord. Loosening its folds she removes the heavy alabaster box with its intricate, inlaid design in lapis lazuli and carries it to where Joseph lies.

Her fingers, trembling with the sorrow

and exhaustion of the last few horrendous hours, she lifts the lid and the small, cramped room is instantly flooded with the fragrance of myrrh: an astringent, bitter-sharp aroma highlighted with a heavy resinous scent of sap seeping from wounded bark and the soft, cool, underlying scent of musty autumnal leaves and deep, cool, black earth.

Balthazar's gift ...

Joseph's old eyes, tired with the strain of trying to see into an unknowable future, momentarily flash with a sudden rush of recollection and the thin, cracked lips part in the shadow of a wistful smile that is so elusive and enigmatic that it might equally have been born of hope or resignation.

With the merest gesture, nothing more than a slight movement of the head upon the pillow, scarcely even a nod, Joseph gives Mary his answer to the last question posed by the visit of those wise men from a lifetime ago ...

Only then does Joseph let go of everything that has held mind and body together for so many years and his eyelids close with a final moth-wing flutter.

When she has laid out and washed the frail husk of human life, Mary takes a little – just a very little – of the myrrh and anoints this man who, for over thirty years, has loyally and lovingly stood by her and her son – *their* son.

Later, Mary will take the remainder of the ointment and give it to the women who plan to go in secret to the borrowed tomb in the garden in order to anoint her son's body for burial.

The last gift is to fulfil its purpose.

Joseph will not see Mary's radiant face

when, on the third day, she hears the story of the empty tomb.

That, however, is of no consequence …

For on this day, the very day on which Joseph's soul slips anchorage, he is met by Jesus, his foster-son – himself both father and son in one person – as he breaks asunder the age-old chains and flings wide the heavy, iron gates of death with his nail-pierced hands.

It is a moment witnessed only by the angels.

Afterword

(to be read afterwards!)

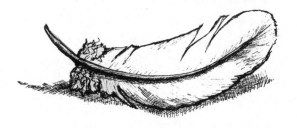

*T*he first thing that must be said about what you have just read is that it is not gospel! Nor is it legend, although it occasionally references legends and draws on a number of ancient traditions. Where people in the story are quoted, I have either used the words found in the King James Bible of 1611 or, where it seemed more apt, the Revised New Jerusalem Bible.

The story itself came to me, as a gift, in a waking dream at Christmastide, in that ancient floating city once known as La Serenissima. Among those who – specifically or indirectly – shaped its telling are, in alphabetical order, Edward Burne-Jones, Frank Capra, Charles Dickens, T. S. Eliot, William Holman Hunt, David Kossoff, C. S. Lewis, John Millais, P. L. Travers and Jane Williams, plus (in their usual, but non-alphabetical, order) Matthew, Mark, Luke and John. The impertinence of attempting to write on behalf of an angel – *and an Archangel at that* – is my own, unaided, folly.

The gift, having been given almost complete and entire, I was left merely to dot the 'i's and cross the 't's. During that process of dotting and crossing, I have immensely benefitted from the thoughts and insights of a group of friends who listened to me talk about the idea or who read it once it got written down and offered encouragement and critique in equally generous measure:

Afterword

Richard Parlour, Pucci Ricci, Sheila Shrigley and Sophie Walpole. I am especially grateful to David Weeks for his unqualified support and, above all, for allowing Joseph to share our Venetian Christmas. Thanks are also due to Nick Clark, Nick and Margaret Hodgson, Phillip Patterson and Fr. Robert Stretton for help and advice.

I am particularly indebted to Bishop Peter Selby, not only for his kind words and wise counsel, but also for introducing me to David Moloney, Editorial Director of Darton, Longman and Todd, who instantly championed this little story and suggested Henry Martin as the perfect artist to decorate it. The final stages in readying the gift was handled with diligence and patience by my editor, Helen Porter, and designer, Judy Linard.

To all of the above I now give back the gift with fond love and deep gratitude.

Brian Sibley
Venice and London